The Noisiest Band in the Land

Mark Nasir

illustrated by Lloyd Lugsden

Rudling House Publishing Limited,

Kemp House, 152 City Road, London EC1V 2NX

Published in the UK in 2015 by Rudling House.

A CIP catalogue record for this book is available from the British Library.

ISBN 978-0-9928689-8-7

Printed in the EU by Little Lamb

www.littlelamb.ro

www.rudlinghouse.com

For our mini-moshers

Ida & Olive

Molly & Rosie

The King was awake and sat up in his bed,
When he smelled eggs and bacon...

"My favourite," he said.

"Breakfast time Queenie! Wake up!" the King roared.
But the Queen just rolled over and continued to snore.

So he banged his royal gong, tried a startling yelp!
He tickled her feet, but none of that helped.
He gave her a nudge, jumped up and screamed "BOO!"
But for all of his efforts, the Queen slept on through.

"Hmmm" the King thought with a clap of his hands,
He summoned the NOISIEST band in the land.

The Musicians arrived, each one of them keen.
"Breakfast is ready, but I can't wake my Queen,
Noisiest Band in the Land...
Would you give me a hand."

"Your Majesty, we have just the song,
Don't worry, this won't take long.
This one's called
'Wake up Queenie, Stop your Royal Snore'.
Everyone ready."

The din was so loud the bed started to **SHAKE**!
But the sleepy Queen still would not wake.

"My eggs and bacon are getting cold,
This just won't do,
Noisiest Band in the Land...
Are you sure there aren't any more of you?"

Then the King thought
and with a clap of his hands,
He summoned all of the Princesses to come
join in with the band.

"Ah, this should be louder than it was before,
Everybody ready." 1, 2, 3, 4!

They all stared at the queen as she opened one eye,
Pulled the sheets over her head then
snuggled up with a sigh.

"My eggs and bacon are getting cold!
This just won't do!
Noisiest Band in the Land...
Are you sure there aren't any more of you?"

With that the King once again clapped his hands,
And summoned all the Princes to come join in
with the band,
"Ah, this should be louder than it was before,
Everybody ready."

1,2,

The King had never heard such a noise before,
And passed out on his pillow and began to snore,
Just as the Queen's alarm clock started to beep,
And slowly she arose from her right royal sleep.

With a stretch and a sniff she sat up in bed,
"Eggs and Bacon, my favourite"
The hungry Queen said.
Then she noticed the King beside her
still snoring.

"Oh breakfast alone can be soooo boring,
Princes, Princesses, Noisiest Band in the Land,
Would you join me for breakfast if you
have nothing else planned?"

So they all sat and ate the Queen's tasty treat, And the sleepy hungry King was left with nothing to eat!

Mark Nasir has spent his adult life writing and performing. Back in the 90's it was all about indie music, sweaty venues and songs of angst. Now in his forties he still performs most days of the week but to a much different audience....Toddlers. He runs his own children's entertainment business...Piccolos Music Club. And it is at his Music club where he finds the inspiration for his stories. Each tale has been tried, tested and fine-tuned on the youngsters that attend his daily sessions. His stories are either performed in song or have a musical theme and many lend themselves to paperback which is where Rudling House got involved. His first book, The Nosiest Band in the Land is a royal tale, with a punk rock twist. A delightfully illustrated book which will appeal to both adults and children alike.

Father of two, Mark lives in rural Bedfordshire from where he operates his business in between school runs. Born and raised in Milton Keynes for 30 years he made the short trip to over the county border and has been there ever since. His songwriting took a distinct change of direction when his two daughters came along and needed entertaining. Silly songs and stories poured from his adoring heart which eventually formed the bare bones of todays Piccolos set list.